Stick to the Script

Compiled
by
Francesca Malloy

Illustrated by Ivan Zamyslov

A 2 Z Press
bestlittleonlinebookstore.com

Stick to the Script

This is a work of fiction.

Printed in the United States of America

A 2 Z Press LLC

PO Box 582 Deleon Springs, FL 32130

bestlittleonlinebookstore.com

sizemore3630@aol.com

440-241-3126

ISBN: 978-1-954191-71-6

Dedicated
to
Mary Christine Malloy
my Ruth

About the Book

The purpose of *Stick to the Script* is to help teach cursive writing. Familiar nursery rhymes are used to facilitate learning to read and write script. The rhymes are in print and below the printed text is the script so that the student can translate instantly and learn to read handwriting easily. Below the handwritten rhyme is a space to practice writing one letter and words containing that letter. Each letter of the alphabet has its own page and an illustration of the rhyme for coloring. Coloring the pictures creates a lingering memory of the lesson it illustrates.

Let ignorance talk as it will, learning has its value.
Jean de La Fontaine, 1679

Contents

A *Ring around the Rosy*   1

B *Little Boy Blue*   3

C *Little Miss Muffet*   5

D *Hickory Dickory Dock*   7

E *Jack Spratt*   9

F *Cat and the Fiddle*   11

G *Girl with a Curl*   13

H *Humpty Dumpty*   15

I *Little Jack Horner*   17

J *Jack and Jill*   19

K *Three Blind Mice*   21

L *Mary Had a Little Lamb*   23

M *Mary, Mary Quite Contrary*   25

N *Jack Be Nimble*   27

O *My Son John*   29

P *Peter, Peter Pumpkin Eater*   31

Q *Queen of Hearts*   33

R *Rock-a-bye Baby*   35

S *Star Light Star Bright*   37

T *Twinkle Twinkle Little Star*   39

U *Banbury Cross*   41

V *Roses are Red*   43

W *Little Bo Peep*   45

X *Sing a Song of Sixpence*   47

Y *Yankee Doodle*   49

Z *Baa Baa Black Sheep*   51

Ring around the rosy
Pocket full of posies
Ashes, ashes
We all fall down.

Ring around the rosy
Pocket full of posies
Ashes, ashes
We all fall down.

a
a
ashes
able
apple

a b c d e f g h i j k l m n o p q r s t u v w x y z

3

Little boy blue
Come blow your horn
The sheep's in the meadow
The cow's in the corn
Where is the little boy
Who tends to the sheep?
He's under the haystack fast asleep.

Little boy blue
Come blow your horn
The sheep's in the meadow
The cow's in the corn
Where is the little boy
Who tends to the sheep?
He's under the haystack
Fast asleep.

B
b
Boy
blue
ball

a b c d e f g h i j k l m n o p q r s t u v w x y z

ABCDEFGHIJKLMNOPQRSTUVWXYZ

Little Miss Muffet
Sat on a tuffet
Eating her curds and whey
Along came a spider
And sat down beside her
And frightened Miss Muffet away.

Little Miss Muffet
Sat on a tuffet
Eating her curds and whey
Along came a spider
And sat down beside her
And frightened Miss Muffet away.

C
c
curds
came
cat

6

a b c d e f g h i j k l m n o p q r s t u v w x y z

7

Hickory dickory dock
The mouse ran up the clock
The clock struck one
And down he come
Hickory dickory dock.

Hickory dickory dock
The mouse ran up the clock
The clock struck one
And down he come
Hickory dickory dock

D
d
dock
down
dog

Jack Spratt could eat no fat,
His wife could eat no lean.
And so between the two of them
They licked the platter clean.

Jack Spratt could eat no fat,
His wife could eat no lean.
And so between the two of them
They licked the platter clean.

E

e

eat

egg

end

ABCDEFGHIJKLMNOPQRSTUVWXYZ

Hey diddle, diddle
The cat and the fiddle
The cow jumped over the moon
The little dog laughed
To see such a sight
And the dish
Ran away with the spoon.

Hey diddle, diddle
The cat and the fiddle
The cow jumped over the moon
The little dog laughed
To see such a sight
And the dish
Ran away with the spoon

F
f
fiddle
face
five

a b c d e f g h i j k l m n o p q r s t u v w x y z

There was a little girl
Who had a little curl
Right in the middle
Of her forehead
When she was good
She was very very good
And when she was bad
She was horrid.

There was a little girl
Who had a little curl
Right in the middle
Of her forehead
When she was good
She was very very good
When she was bad
She was horrid.

G
g
girl
good
green

14

a b c d e f g h i j k l m n o p q r s t u v w x y z

a b c d e f g h i j k l m n o p q r s t u v w x y z

15

A B C D E F G H I J K L M N O P Q R S T U V W X Y Z

Humpty Dumpty
Sat on a wall
Humpty Dumpty
Had a great fall
All the king's horses
And all the king's men
Couldn't put Humpty Dumpty
Together again.

Humpty Dumpty
Sat on a wall
Humpty Dumpty
Had a great fall
All the kings horses
And all the kings men
Couldn't put Humpty Dumpty
Together again

H
h
Humpty
horses
had

16

Little Jack Horner
Sat in a corner
Eating his Christmas pie.
He stuck in his thumb
And pulled out a plum
And said, "What a good boy am I."

Little Jack Horner
Sat in a corner
Eating his Christmas pie.
He stuck in his thumb
And pulled out a plum
And said, "What a good boy am I."

I
i
in
idea
Indian

ABCDEFGHIJKLMNOPQRSTUVWXYZ

Jack and Jill
Went up the hill
To fetch a pail of water
Jack fell down
And broke his crown
And Jill came tumbling after.

Jack and Jill
Went up the hill
To fetch a pail of water
Jack fell down
And broke his crown
And Jill came tumbling after

J j
jump
juice
Jack

abcdefghijklmnopqrstuvwxyz

Three blind mice, three blind mice
See how they run, see how they run
They all ran after the farmer's wife
Who cut off their tails
With a carving knife.
Did you ever see such
A sight in your life
As three blind mice.

Three blind mice, three blind mice
See how they run, see how they run
They all ran after the farmers wife
Who cut off their tails
With a carving knife.
Did you ever see such
A sight in your life
As three blind mice.

X
k
knife
kite
kick

abcdefghijklmnopqrstuvwxyz

abcdefghijklmnopqrstuvwxyz

ABCDEFGHIJKLMNOPQRSTUVWXYZ

Mary had a little lamb
Its fleece was white as snow
And everywhere that Mary went
The lamb was sure to go.
It followed her to school one day
Which was against the rule.
It made the children laugh and play
To see a lamb at school.

Mary had a little lamb
Its fleece was white as snow
And everywhere that Mary went
The lamb was sure to go.
It followed her to school one day
Which was against the rule.
It made the children laugh + play
To see a lamb at school.

L
l
lamb
little
laugh

Mary, Mary quite contrary
How does your garden grow?
With silver bells and cockle shells
And pretty maids in a row.

Mary, Mary quite contrary
How does your garden grow?
With silver bells and cockle shells
And pretty maids in a row.

M

m

Mary

maids

more

a b c d e f g h i j k l m n o p q r s t u v w x y z

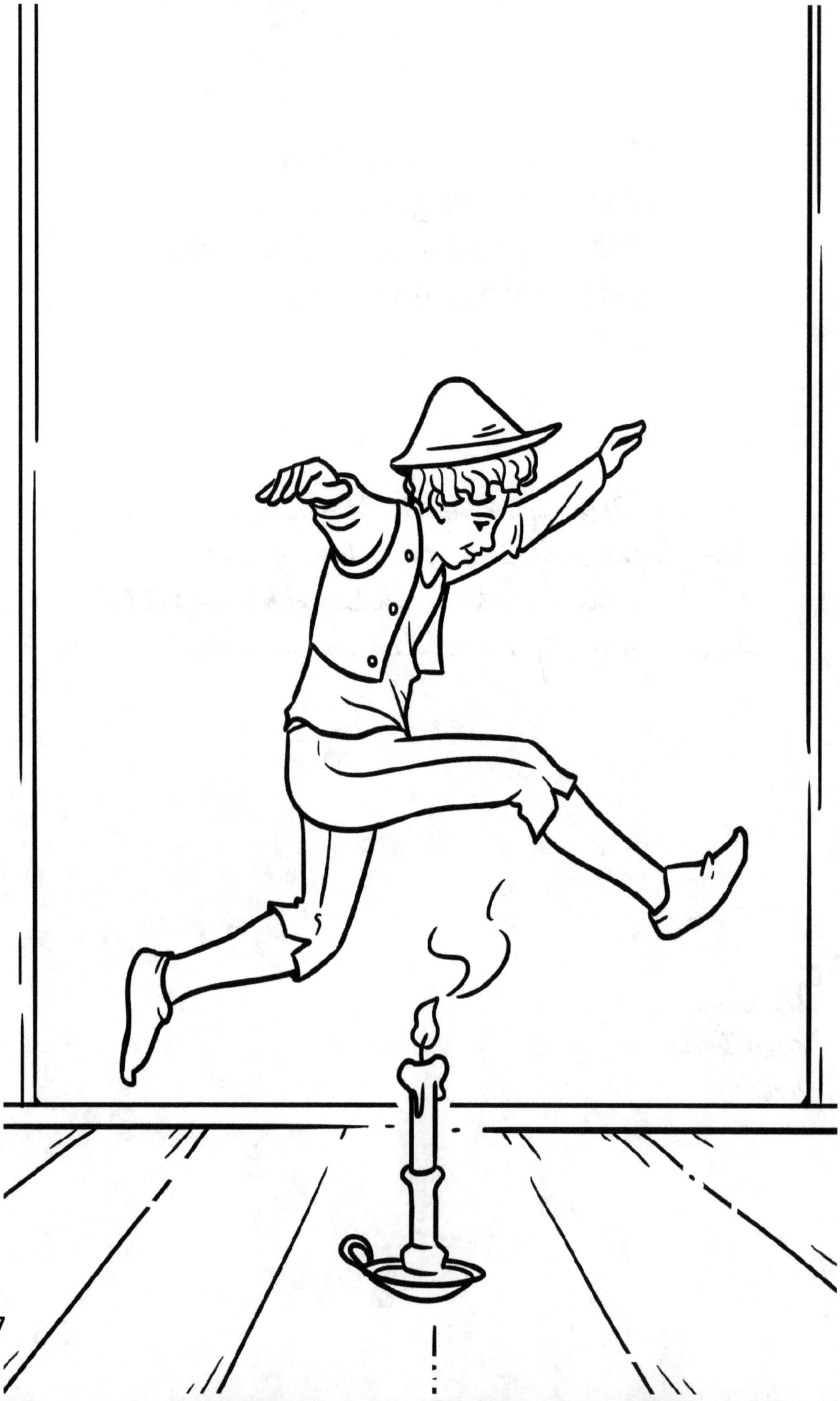

ABCDEFGHIJKLMNOPQRSTUVWXYZ

Jack be nimble
Jack be quick
Jack jump over
The candlestick.

Jack be nimble
Jack be quick
Jack jump over
The candlestick

n

n

nimble

note

nest

Diddle, diddle dumplin
My son John
Went to bed
With his stockings on
One shoe off and one shoe on
Diddle, diddle dumplin
My son John.

Diddle, diddle dumplin
My son John
Went to bed
With his stockings on
One shoe off and one shoe on
Diddle, diddle dumplin
My son John.

O
o
off
on
one

Peter, Peter, pumpkin eater
Had a wife but couldn't keep her.
Put her in a pumpkin shell,
And there he kept her very well.

Peter, Peter, pumpkin eater
Had a wife and couldn't keep her.
Put her in a pumkin shell,
And there he kept her very well.

P

p
pumpkin
pony
play

abcdefghijklmnopqrstuvwxyz

The Queen of Hearts
She made some tarts
All on a summer's day.
The Knave of Hearts
He stole the tarts
And took them clean away.

The Queen of Hearts
She made some tarts
All on a summers day.
The Knave of Hearts
He stole the tarts
And took them clean away.

Q
q
Queen
quilt
quick

Rock-a-bye baby
On the tree tops
When the wind blows
The cradle will rock
When the bough breaks
The cradle will fall
And down will came baby
Cradle and all.

Rock-a-bye baby
On the tree top
When the wind blows
The cradle will rock
When the bough breaks
The cradle will fall
And down will come baby
Cradle and all.

R

r

rock

ran

ride

a b c d e f g h i j k l m n o p q r s t u v w x y z

a b c d e f g h i j k l m n o p q r s t u v w x y z

Star light, star bright
First star I see tonight
I wish I may
I wish I might
Have the Wish
I wish tonight.

Star light, star bright
First star I see tonight
I wish I may
I wish I might
Have the Wish
I wish tonight.

I

s

star

see

sat

ABCDEFGHIJKLMNOPQRSTUVWXYZ

Twinkle, twinkle little star
How I wonder what you are
Up above the world so high
Like a diamond in the sky.

Twinkle, twinkle little star
How I wonder what you are
Up above the world so high
Like a diamond in the sky.

T
t
twinkle
train
two

Ride a cock horse
To Banbury Cross
To see an old lady
Upon a white horse
Rings on her fingers
And bells on her toes
She will have music
Wherever she goes.

Ride a cock horse
To Banbury Cross
To see an old lady
Upon a white horse
Rings on her fingers
And bells on her toes
She will have music
Wherever she goes.

U

u

upon

under

umbrella

a b c d e f g h i j k l m n o p q r s t u v w x y z

A B C D E F G H I J K L M N O P Q R S T U V W X Y Z

Roses are red
Violets are blue
Sugar is sweet
And so are you.

Roses are red
Violets are blue
Sugar is sweet
And so are you.

V

v

violets

voice

very

44

Little Bo-Peep
Has lost her sheep
And doesn't know
Where to find them
Leave them alone
And they will come home
Wagging their tails behind them.

Little Bo-Peep
Has lost her sheep
And doesn't know
Where to find them
Leave them alone
And they'll come home
Wagging their tails behind them.

W
w
wind
west
wag

ABCDEFGHIJKLMNOPQRSTUVWXYZ

Sing a song of sixpence
Pocket full of rye
Four and twenty blackbirds
Baked in a pie.
When the pie was opened
The birds began to sing.
Wasn't that a dainty dish
To set before the king?

Sing a song of sixpence
Pocket full of rye
Four and twenty blackbirds
Baked in a pie.
When the pie was opened
The birds began to sing.
Wasn't that a dainty dish
To set before the king?

X
x
x-ray
six
extra

a b c d e f g h i j k l m n o p q r s t u v w x y z

a b c d e f g h i j k l m n o p q r s t u v w x y z

Yankee Doodle
Went to town
Riding on a pony.
Stuck a feather in his hat
And called it macaroni.

Yankee Doodle
Went to town
Riding on a pony.
Stuck a feather in his hat
And called it macaroni.

Y
y
you
yes
Yankee

A B C D E F G H I J K L M N O P Q R S T U V W X Y Z

Baa baa black sheep
Have you any wool
Yes sir, yes sir
Three bags full
One for my master
One for my dame
One for the little boy
Who lives down the lane.

Baa baa black sheep
Have you any wool
Yes sir, yes sir
Three bags full
One for my master
One for my dame
One for the little boy
Who lives down the lane.

z
z
zero
zipper
zoo

Acknowledgements

My thanks to my faithful assistant Jessica Morris, always at hand with a solution to my problems, always ready to jump in with a word that is tantalizing and eluding me. My thanks also to Lee Sizemore, my publisher, whose attention to detail pulled this book together. And finally to Mary Malloy for suggesting the title of this book and for her ever endearing encouragement.

About the Creator of this Book

Francesca Malloy was born in 1923 and she has compiled this book to celebrate her 100th birthday coming up. Her first career was as a dancer. She was a chorus girl in a USO troop entertaining soldiers, sailors, and marines in WWII.

In 1956 Francesca started on a long journey to get a formal education. In 1965 she earned her Bachelor's Degree from New York University. In 1972 she received her Master's Degree from Hunter College of the City University of New York, and in 1979 she completed her Juris Doctorate degree from St. John's University. All of her classes were taken in night school. She has been an inspiration to friends and family.

Francesca taught English for 20 years in New York City middle and high schools and practiced law for 20 years in Brooklyn, New York. She had 5 children. Her loving son Sean, a mathematics professor, passed away in 2014. She has 4 living children, 13 grandchildren, and 9 great-grandchildren.

CPSIA information can be obtained
at www.ICGtesting.com
Printed in the USA
LVHW062049221022
731329LV00016B/922

9 781954 191716